THE KRAKEN

Written by Carrie Lewis

Ben Tennyson
Ben can use the Omnitrix to turn into many super aliens!
Gwen
Ben's cousin
Grandpa Max

SUPER ALIENS
Stinkfly
Ripjaw
THE BAD GUY
Jonah

Ben, Gwen and Grandpa were camping by a lake for the weekend.

One morning, Grandpa and Ben went fishing with Captain Shaw. The Captain told them he was hunting for a monster that lived in the lake. It was called the Krakken.

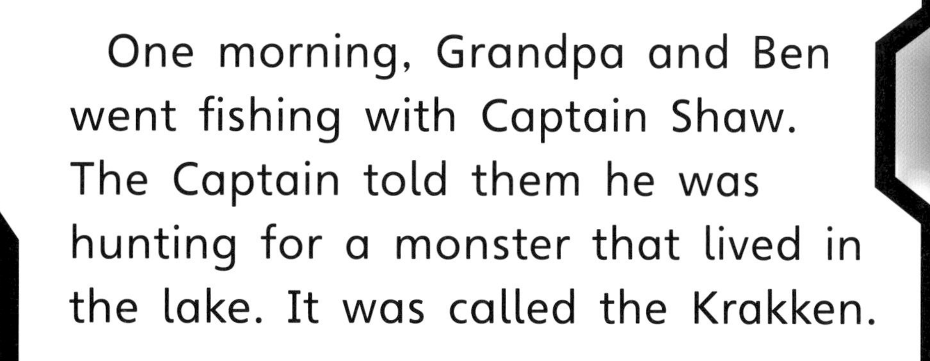

Back at camp, Ben and Grandpa were talking.

"Captain Shaw wants to hunt for the Krakken," said Ben, "and I want to help him!"

"We are not chasing monsters!" said Grandpa.

That night Ben ran away to the Captain's boat. The Captain agreed that Ben could go with him to hunt for the Krakken.

Captain Shaw dived into the lake and Ben followed him.
At the bottom of the lake they found an enormous egg. It was one of the Krakken's eggs!

Soon they came up for air,
but some bad men were waiting
for the Captain. Ben hid.
The men wanted to
steal the Krakken's eggs.

The leader of the bad men took off his mask.

"Take the Captain away," he said. "We will come back later to get the eggs."

The men took Captain Shaw away. Meanwhile, Ben used the Omnitrix to transform into Stinkfly. He chased the men onto their boat.

When the men saw Stinkfly,
they threw Captain Shaw
into the water.
Stinkfly pulled the Captain
out just in time.

As soon as they got back to Grandpa's camper van, the Rust Bucket, Stinkfly transformed back into Ben.

Ben told the others about the eggs in the lake.

"The eggs belong to the Krakken. Those men are going to steal them!" he said.

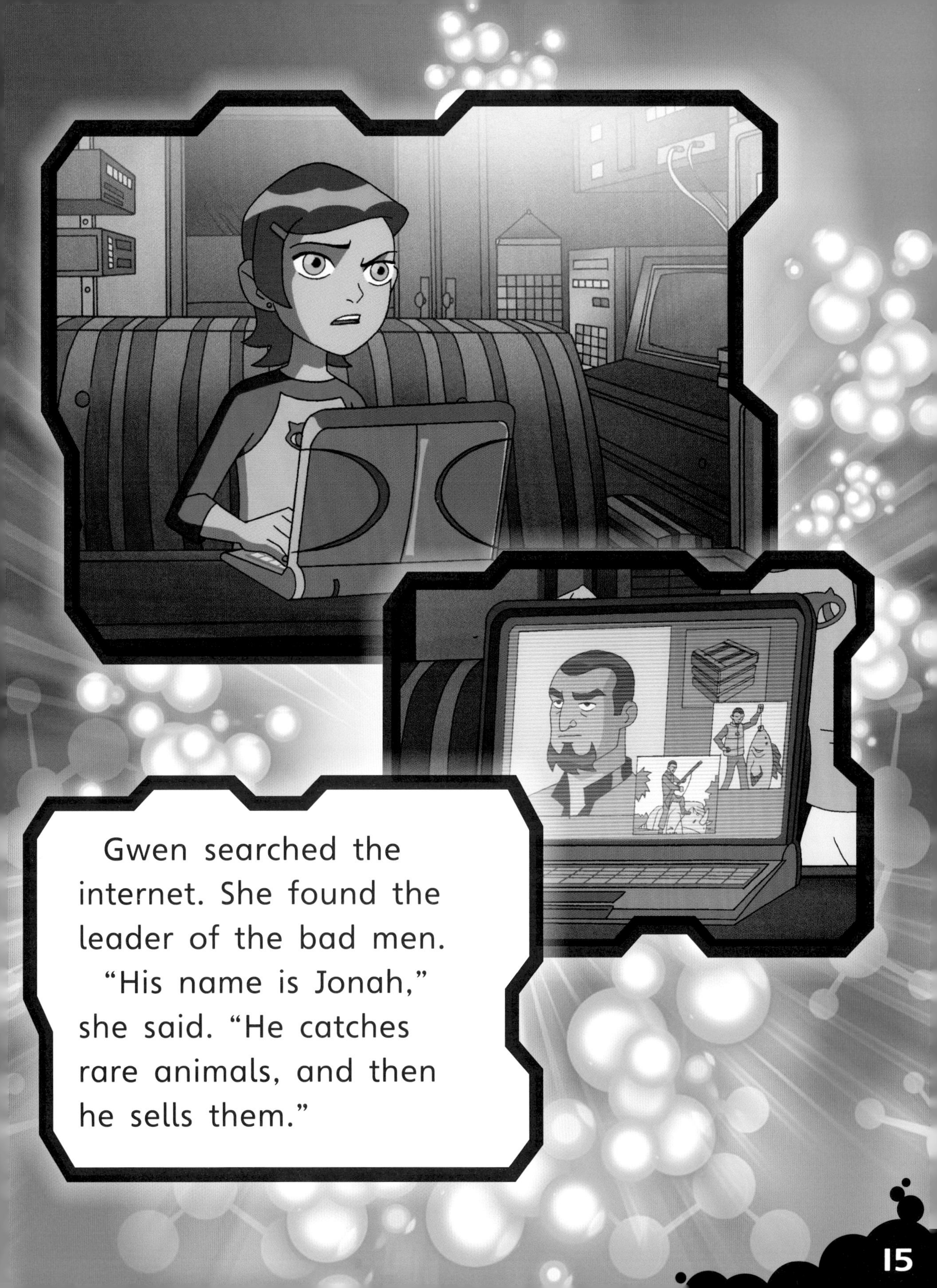
Gwen searched the internet. She found the leader of the bad men.
"His name is Jonah," she said. "He catches rare animals, and then he sells them."

Ben, Gwen and Grandpa set off in Captain Shaw's rowing boat.

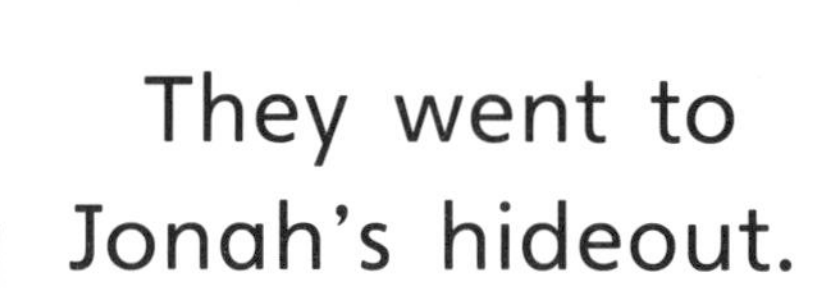

They went to Jonah's hideout.

Meanwhile, Jonah had been busy. He had taken the Krakken's eggs.

Suddenly, Jonah and his men saw the Krakken. It was coming to attack them because they had stolen its eggs.

Jonah would not let go of the eggs because he was using them to trap the Krakken.

Ben used the Omnitrix to become Ripjaw. He grabbed the eggs from Jonah.

Ripjaw dived into the water and took the eggs back to the Krakken's nest.

The Krakken had her eggs back.

Meanwhile, Jonah did not get away. Ripjaw watched him until the police came to arrest him.

Soon Captain Shaw arrived. He thought he had got the Krakken in his net ...
... but it turned out to be Ben!